THE Twelve Days of Christmas

THE Twelve

For Lia

Illustrated by JAN BRETT

Days of Christmas

PAPERSTAR

The Putnam & Grosset Group

THE TWELVE DAYS

English traditional carol

VERSES 1-4

1. On the first* day of Christ-mas my
2. On the se-cond* day of Christ-mas my

true love gave to me a
true love gave to me

4 3 2 1

four col-ly birds, three French hens, two tur-tle-doves,
four three _ two
and a par-tridge in a pear tree.

VERSES 5-12

12

5. On the fifth* day of Christ-mas my true love gave to me twelve lords a-leap-ing,
6. On the sixth* day of Christ-mas my true love gave to me twelve

*Sing appropriate number of day, and then cut from † to appropriate boxed number.

OF CHRISTMAS

On the first day of Christmas

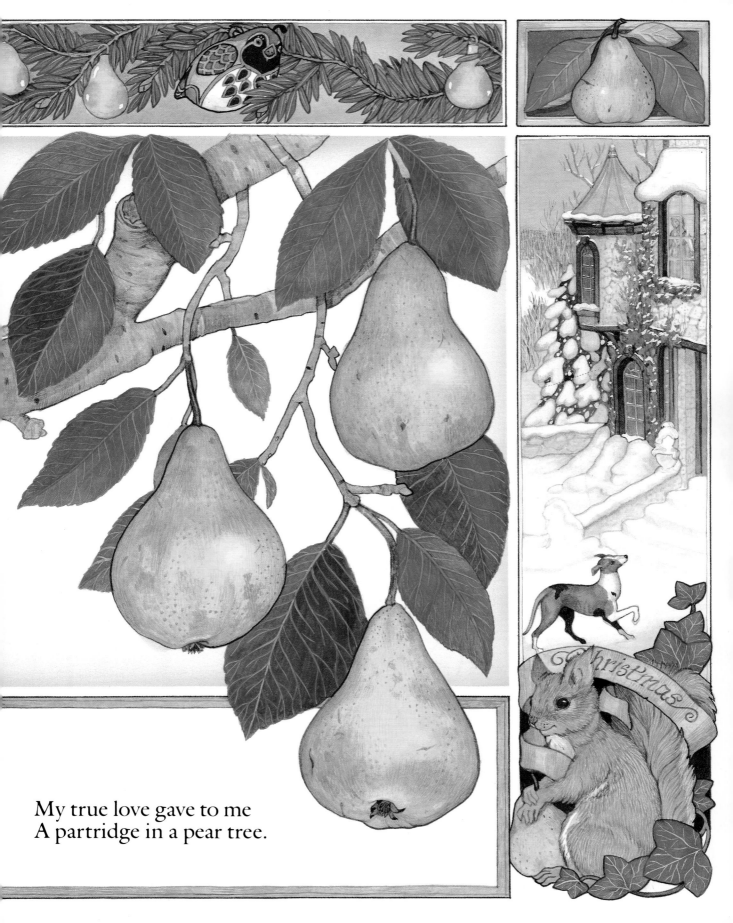

My true love gave to me
A partridge in a pear tree.

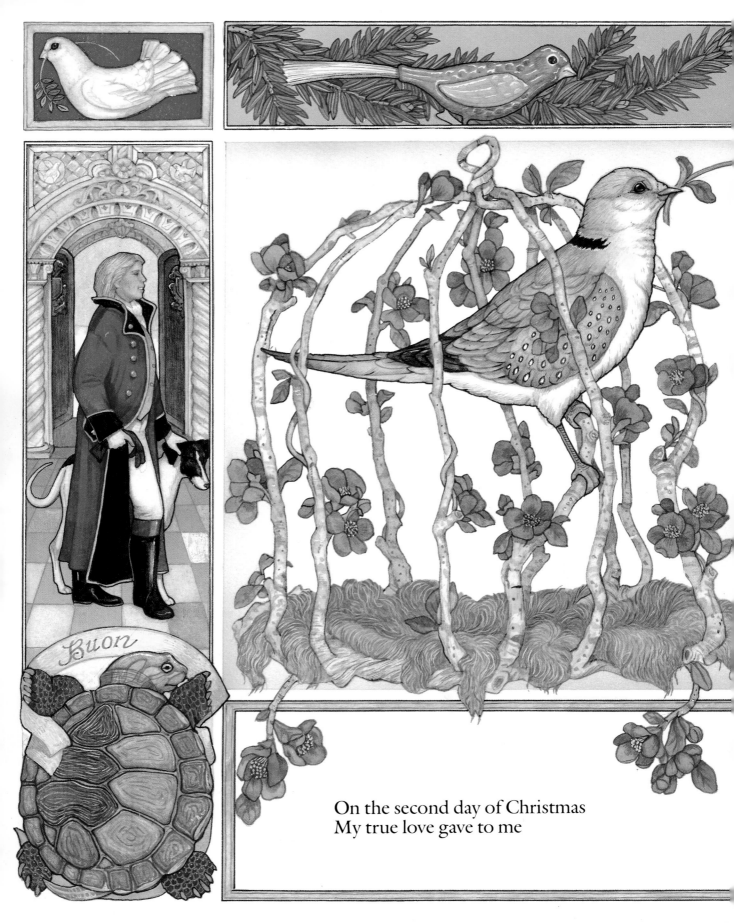

Buon

On the second day of Christmas
My true love gave to me

Two turtledoves,
And a partridge in a pear tree.

Joyeux

On the third day of Christmas
My true love gave to me
Three French hens,

Two turtledoves,
And a partridge in a pear tree.

On the fourth day of Christmas
My true love gave to me
Four colly birds,

Three French hens,
Two turtledoves,
And a partridge in a pear tree.

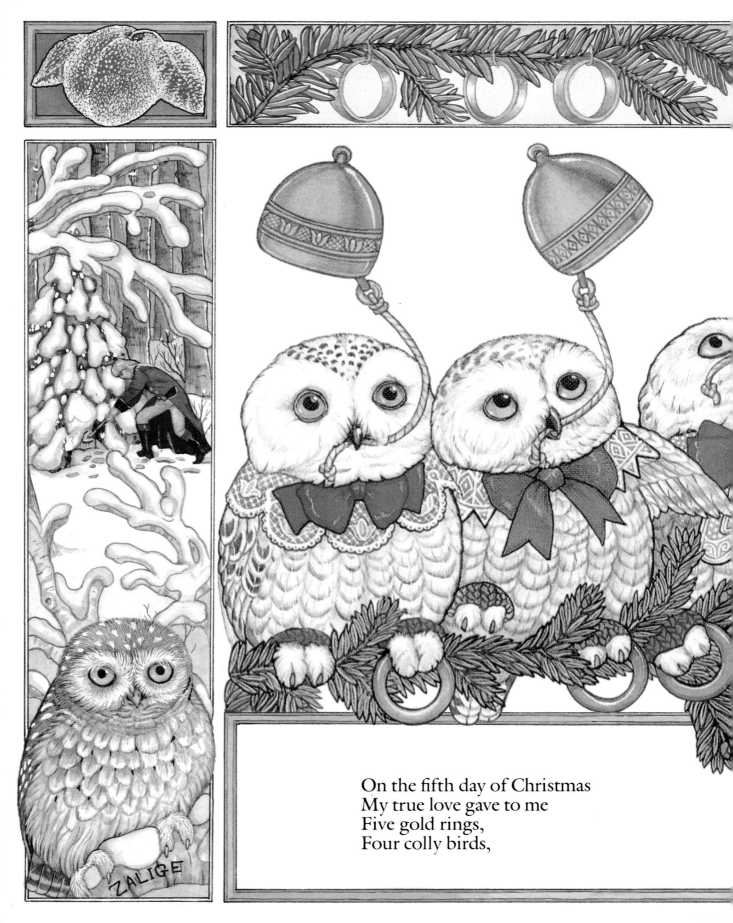

On the fifth day of Christmas
My true love gave to me
Five gold rings,
Four colly birds,

Three French hens,
Two turtledoves,
And a partridge in a pear tree.

KERSTDAGEN

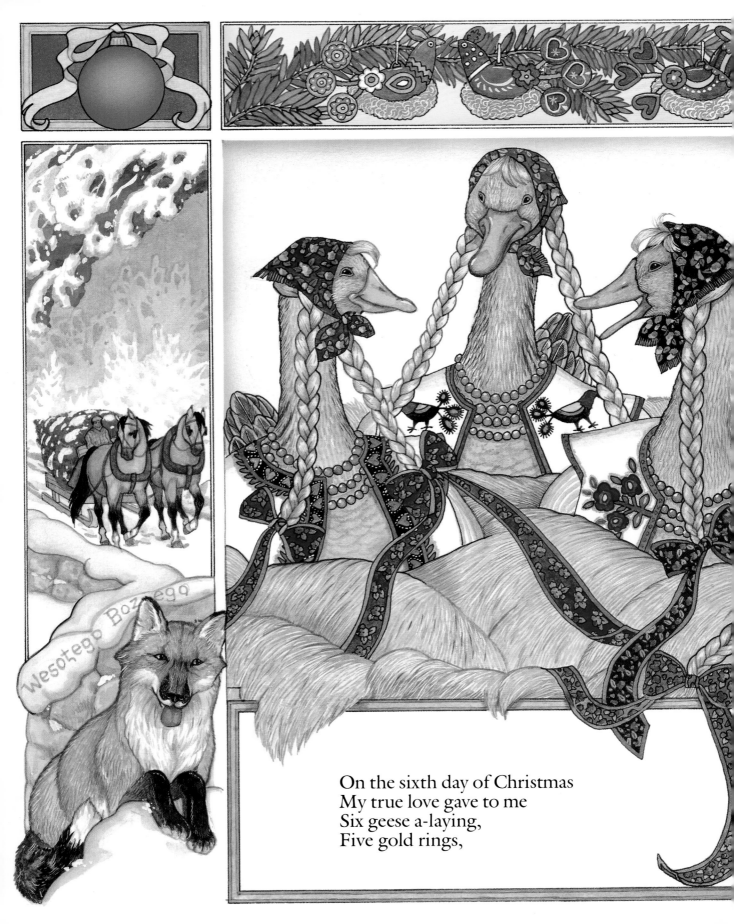

On the sixth day of Christmas
My true love gave to me
Six geese a-laying,
Five gold rings,

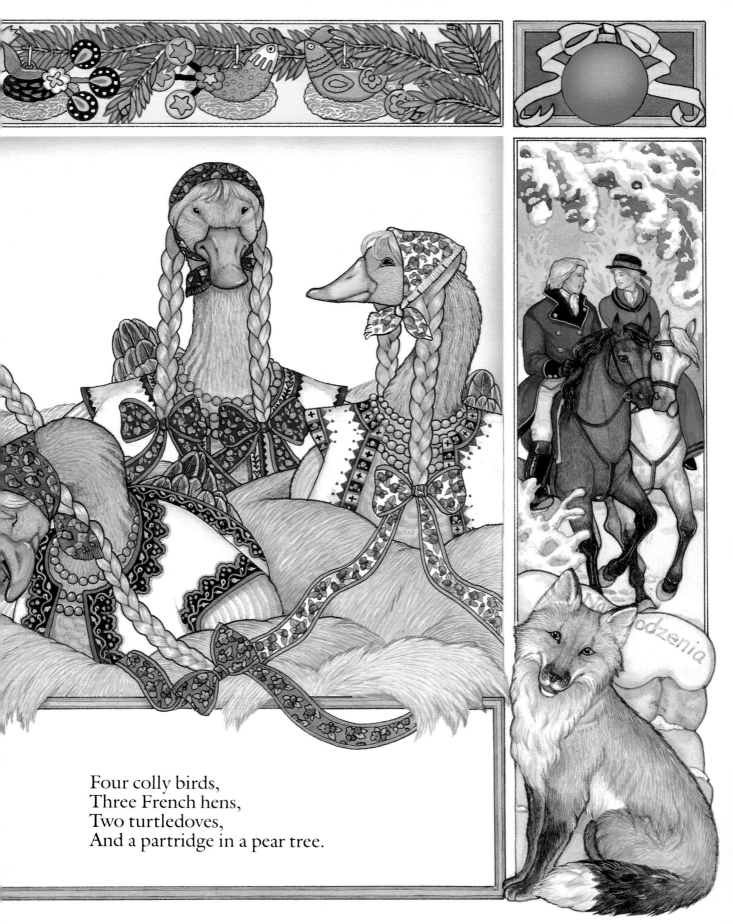

Four colly birds,
Three French hens,
Two turtledoves,
And a partridge in a pear tree.

СЧАСТЛИВОГО

On the seventh day of Christmas
My true love gave to me
Seven swans a-swimming,
Six geese a-laying,
Five gold rings,

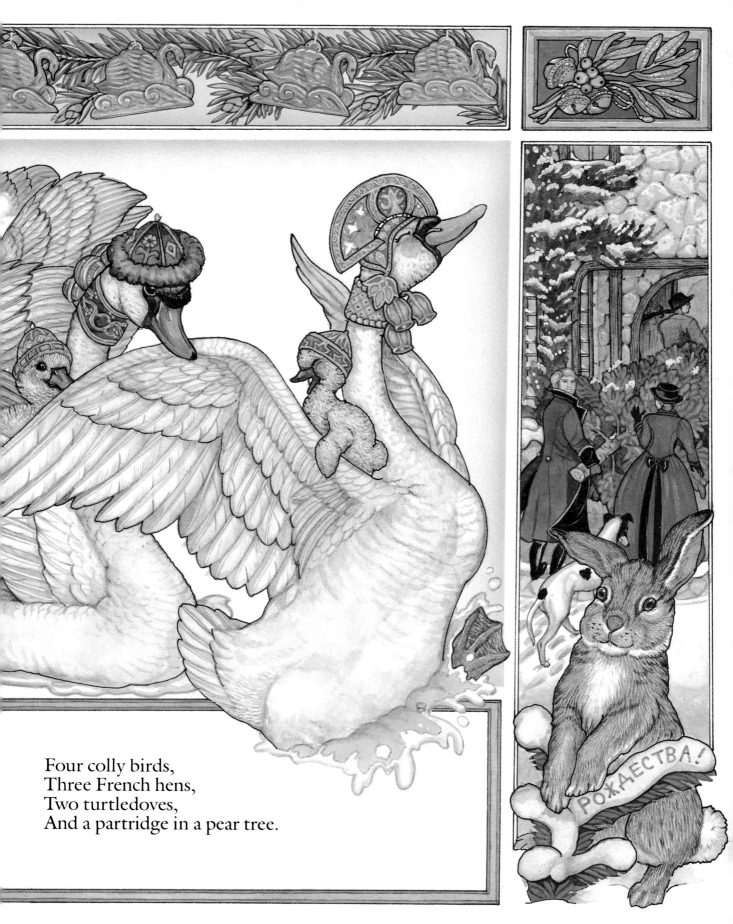

Four colly birds,
Three French hens,
Two turtledoves,
And a partridge in a pear tree.

РОЖДЕСТВА!

On the eighth day of Christmas
My true love gave to me
Eight maids a-milking,
Seven swans a-swimming,
Six geese a-laying,

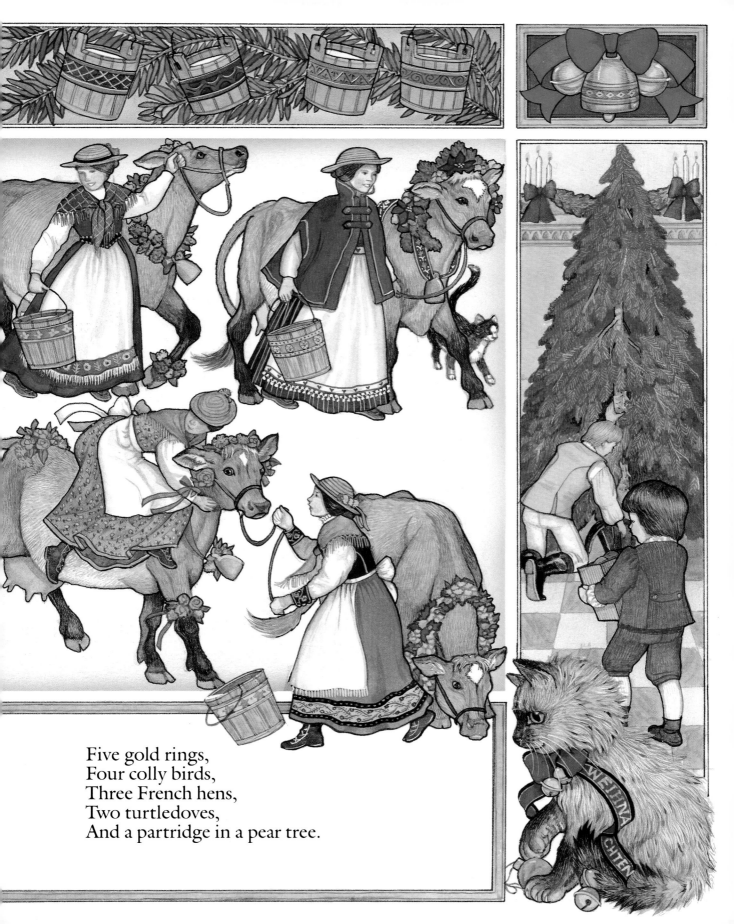

Five gold rings,
Four colly birds,
Three French hens,
Two turtledoves,
And a partridge in a pear tree.

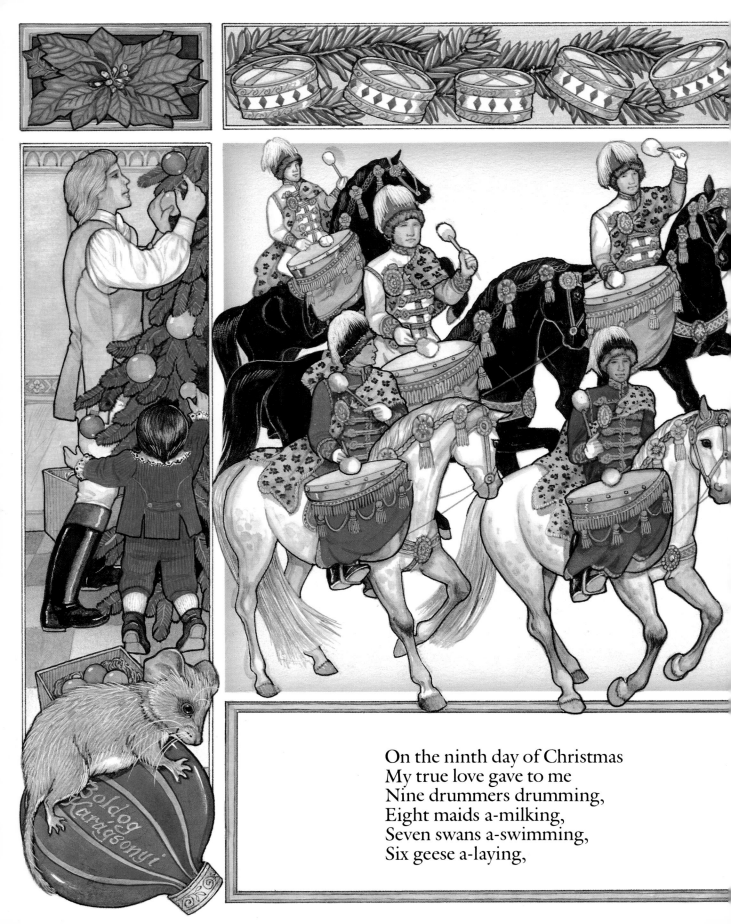

On the ninth day of Christmas
My true love gave to me
Nine drummers drumming,
Eight maids a-milking,
Seven swans a-swimming,
Six geese a-laying,

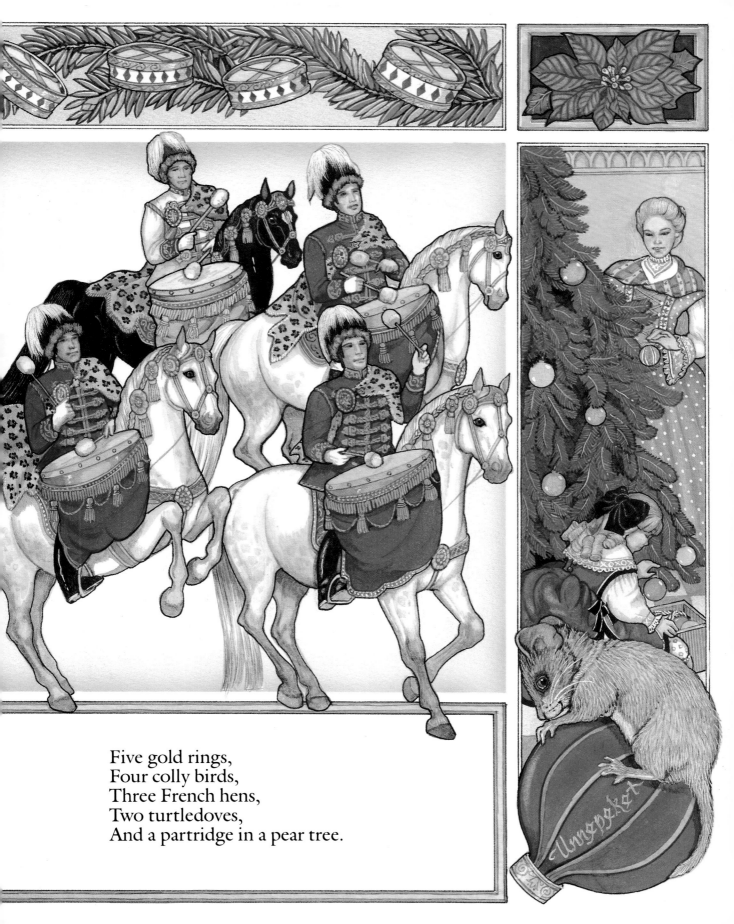

Five gold rings,
Four colly birds,
Three French hens,
Two turtledoves,
And a partridge in a pear tree.

On the tenth day of Christmas
My true love gave to me
Ten pipers piping,
Nine drummers drumming,
Eight maids a-milking,
Seven swans a-swimming,

Six geese a-laying,
Five gold rings,
Four colly birds,
Three French hens,
Two turtledoves,
And a partridge in a pear tree.

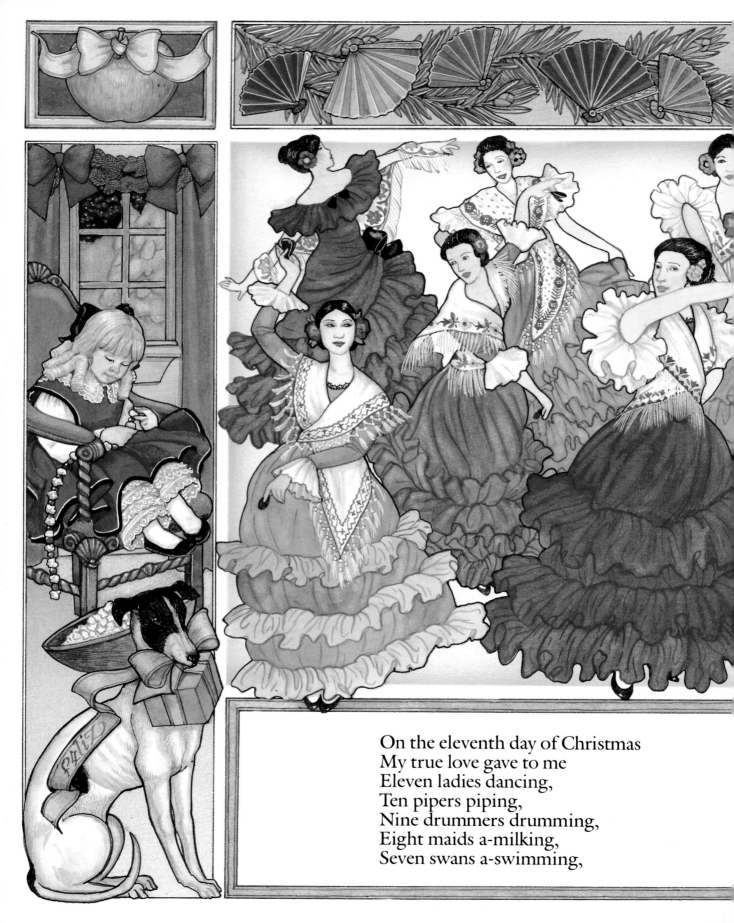

On the eleventh day of Christmas
My true love gave to me
Eleven ladies dancing,
Ten pipers piping,
Nine drummers drumming,
Eight maids a-milking,
Seven swans a-swimming,

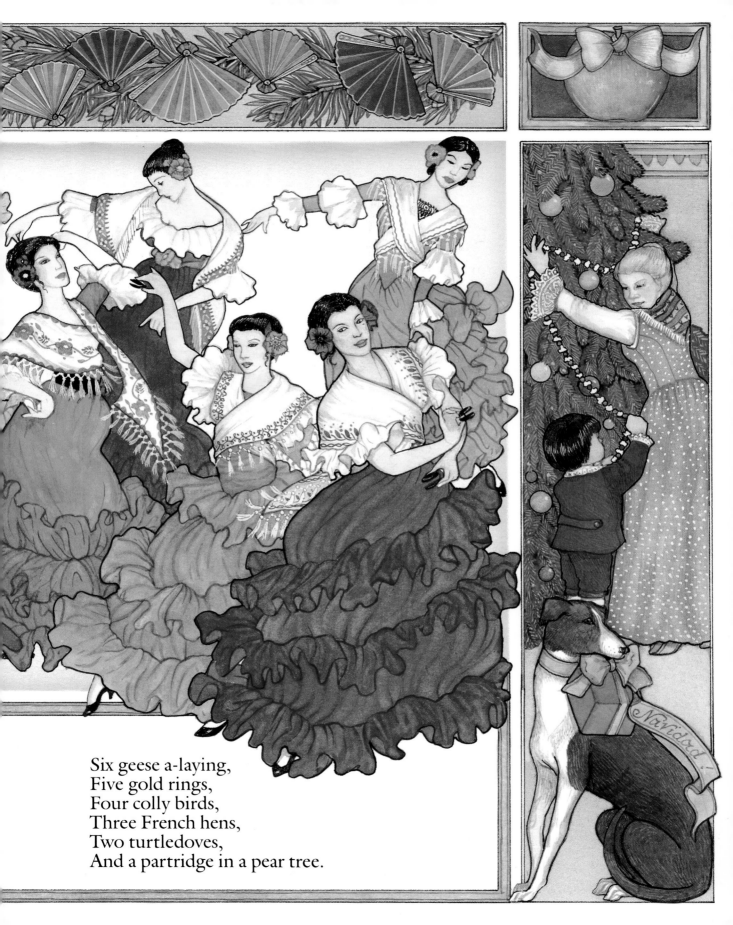

Six geese a-laying,
Five gold rings,
Four colly birds,
Three French hens,
Two turtledoves,
And a partridge in a pear tree.

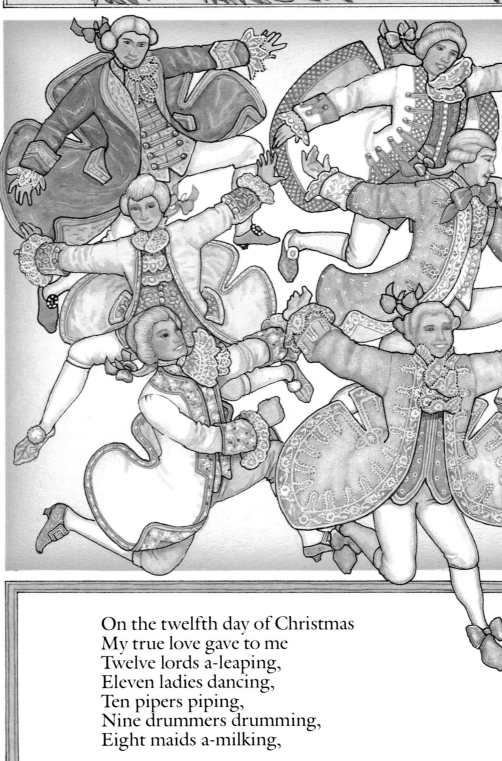

On the twelfth day of Christmas
My true love gave to me
Twelve lords a-leaping,
Eleven ladies dancing,
Ten pipers piping,
Nine drummers drumming,
Eight maids a-milking,

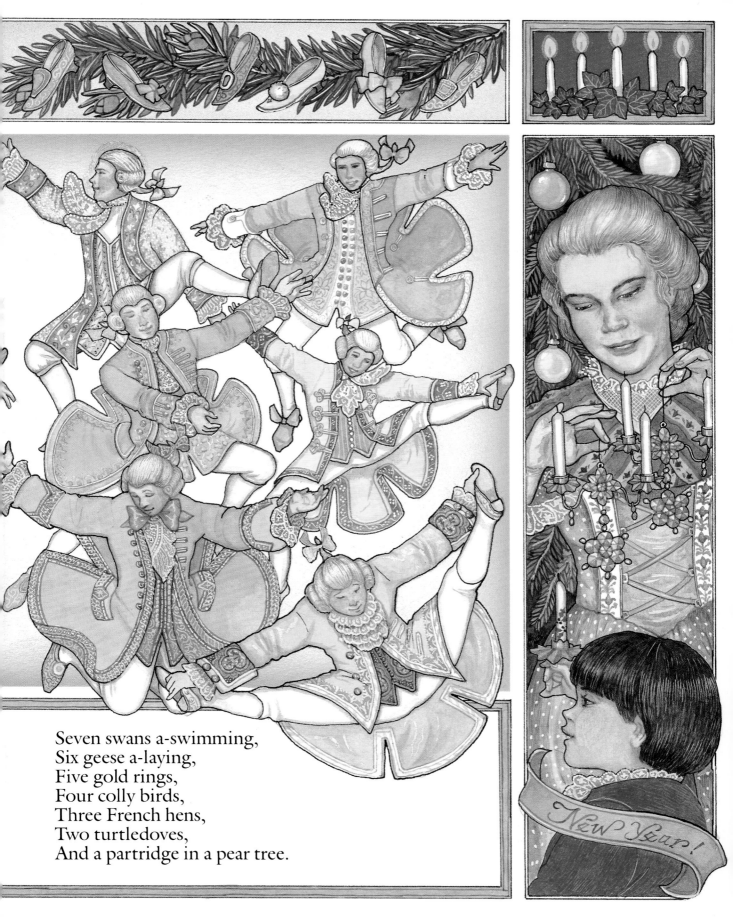

Seven swans a-swimming,
Six geese a-laying,
Five gold rings,
Four colly birds,
Three French hens,
Two turtledoves,
And a partridge in a pear tree.

New Year!

Editor's Note

The Twelve Days of Christmas—the days linking Christmas on December 25 and the Epiphany on January 6 (when the three Magi offered the first Christmas presents—gold, frankincense, and myrrh) were declared a festal tide (religious holiday) by the Council of Tours in 567. Since then it has been a time when noble and peasant alike put work aside and enjoyed an extended holiday of feasting, celebration, and sharing with others. It was considered bad luck to enter someone's house empty-handed.

The ancient counting song named for this religious holiday is actually quite pagan in tone and is the only carol we know that celebrates, in the form of a list, the Christmas tradition of gift-giving. It is said to date back to a thirteenth century manuscript in the Library of Trinity College, Cambridge, England. The carol appeared in print for the first time in a children's book entitled, *Mirth Without Mischief,* published in London about 1780.

"The Twelve Days of Christmas" became very popular as a game song—usually played at a large gathering of children and adults on the Twelfth Day night, just before the eating of mince pie. With the company seated all around the room, the leader of the game began by singing the first day lines, which were then repeated by each of the company in turn. Then the first day lines were repeated with the addition of the second day lines by the leader, and this was repeated by all in turn. This continued until all the lines of the twelve days were repeated by everyone. If anyone missed a line, they would have to forfeit something of theirs to the group.

Illustrations copyright © 1986 by Jan Brett
All rights reserved. This book, or parts thereof, may not be reproduced in any form without
permission in writing from the publisher. A PaperStar Book, published in 1997 by
The Putnam & Grosset Group, 200 Madison Avenue, New York, NY 10016.
PaperStar Books is a registered trademark of The Putnam Berkley Group, Inc.
The PaperStar logo is a trademark of The Putnam Berkley Group, Inc.
Originally published in 1986 by Dodd, Mead & Co.
Published simultaneously in Canada. Manufactured in China
Music adapted from Carols for Christmas, compiled by David Willcocks.
Copyright © 1983 by The Metropolitan Museum of Art.
Reprinted by permission of Henry Holt and Company, Inc.

Library of Congress Cataloging-in-Publication Data
The twelve days of Christmas.
Summary: A young woman's true love sends her extravagant
gifts on each of the twelve days of Christmas.
1. Folk songs, English—Texts. 2. Christmas music. [1. Folk songs, English.
2. Christmas music.] I. Brett, Jan, ill. II. Title: 12 days of Christmas.
PZ8. 3.T8516 1989 784.4 05 89-43065
ISBN 0-698-11569-4
5 7 9 10 8 6